Fauna of the Caribbean

The Last Survivors

Lesley Sutty

CARIBBEAN

First published 1993 by
MACMILLAN EDUCATION LTD
London and Basingstoke
Companies and representatives throughout the world

ISBN 0–333–55877–4

11	10	9	8	7	6	5	4	3	2
06	05	04	03	02	01	00	99	98	97

This book is printed on paper suitable for recycling and
made from fully managed and sustained forest sources.

Printed in Hong Kong

A catalogue record for this book is available from the
British Library.

*To Rocky, Missie and Silver, and those
who made their freedom possible.*

Contents

Acknowledgements

I wish to express my gratitude to those who encouraged and assisted me in so many different ways, to accomplish this work.

John ALBANIE, President of the Grenada Society for the Prevention of Cruelty to Animals, Grenada.

Peggy ALCOTT, James Martin JONES, Ivan HATTINGH, Jane GREY-EDWARDS, Jean-Paul RENARD and Indrani LUTCHMAN of the Worldwide Fund for Nature, (WWF), UK

Lynne-Rose BEUZE, Head of the Cultural Heritage Office and Museum, Martinique

Allissandra CUMMINS and Phillipa NEWTON, Curators of the Barbados National Museum

Madeleine DE GRANDMAISON, President of the Cultural and Environmental Commission, Martinique

Marydele DONELLEY and Nina YOUNG of the Centre for Marine Conservation, (CMC), Washington

Russell FORGHAM, Managing Editor of the Mail On Sunday, UK

John FULLER, Antigua International Whaling Commission Representative (IWC)

Calvin HOWELL and David SIMMONS of the Caribbean Conservation Association, (CCA), Barbados

Virginia McKENNA and Sheila RUSSELL, Into The Blue and Zoo Check, UK

Tony MIGNUCCI, Director of the Caribbean Stranding Network, Puerto Rico

Desmond and Lisa NICHOLSON, Curators of the Antigua National Museum

Bernard PETITJEAN-ROGET, Robert, Martinique

Steven PRICE, University of Davis, California

Yves RENARD, International Union for the Conservation of Nature, St. Lucia

Miguel RODRIGUEZ, Director of the Institute of Puerto Rican Culture, Puerto Rico

Jean-Jacques SEYMOUR, Radio Caribbean International, Martinique

Sally SHOUP and Gerry LEAP, GREENPEACE, Washington

Mike SUTTON and Sally RUSSELL of the Worldwide Fund for Nature (WWF), Washington

Will TRAVERS, Born Free Foundation, UK

Craig VAN NORT of Monitor Consortium International, Washington

Kay WHITESIDE, Marie BEST and Anita GOLDBERG, Universal Charities

Mary Ann WRIGHT of the USA Embassy Grenada and Washington

Larry ZIMMERMAN, Vermillion University

The author and publishers would like to acknowledge with thanks the following photographic sources:

John E ALBANIE, GSPCA, pp.84, 85
John BAINBRIDGE, WWF, Washington p.24, bottom left
Leo BATTEN, Frank Lane Picture Agency p.49
R O BIERREGAARD, WWF, Washington p.67
CENTRE FOR MARINE CONSERVATION, Washington pp.6 bottom right, 86
Hans Dieter BRANDL, Frank Lane Picture Agency p.78
John DORMONT, CMC p.15
Wohlwender, ENVIRONMENTAL INVESTIGATION AGENCY p.14
Mark J FERRARI, WWF, Washington p.12, top left and right
Antonio A Mignucci GIANNONI p.vii
J P GEOFFROY, AADN pp.58, 82
Deborah GLOCKNER-FERRARI, WWF, Washington pp.9, 11, 19, top
Eric & David HOSKING, Frank Lane Picture Agency p.45
James HUDNALL, CMC p.12, bottom

George H H HUEY, WWF, Washington pp.22, 25
Chris HUXLEY pp.3, top right, 31, 32, 61, 73
JACANA Photo Agency pp.39, 40
Daphne KINZLER, Frank Lane Picture Agency p.51, top
G W LENNOX pp.48, 72
The MAIL ON SUNDAY p.iii
Michael MAJOR, CMC p.27
R McDERMOTT, CMC p.63
R A MITTERMEIER, WWF, Washington pp.24, top, 66
Jill PERRY, CMC p.7, top left
D & N POPOV p.29, 43, 55, 58, top, 81, 83
PORTECOP p.71, bottom
POST OFFICE OF BARBADOS and the CROWN AGENTS STAMP BUREAU pp.69, 74
J POWELL, WWF, Washington p.2
Peter PRITCHARD p.22
Jim SERTIS, CMC p.20
J SMITH, WWF p.64
Nadine ZUBER, WWF, Washington p.24, bottom right

Foreword

When I set sail from the coast of North Africa in the winter of 1968 bound for the West Indies, my eyes searched a fading blue and mauve horizon for hours, as the sun set on a land of a thousand African animals. Many of them I had nurtured and loved; jackals, fennics, rapalmists. Some weeks later my desert dog and I observed a new, luxuriant and exuberant land; a Caribbean island. Tired of Atlantic swells, my dog quit me and swam fast and earnestly towards these new shores. As fate would have it she encountered only other foreign members of her kind; a bad tempered baboon from Addis Ababa, a rabbit from Serbia and a dexterous mongoose from India. They scavenged our yard and ruled our home, eventually with a more local fauna.

The giant blue land crabs; the transparent, fragile reinette climbing frog whose chant filled our warm night air; the nocturnal wanderer, the armadillo; and their many allies in the sea. To whom should I dedicate this endeavour I asked myself; to all or one? For each was an unending source of learning.

In May 1991 came a glimmer of hope for the survival of our fauna; the return of the dolphins Rocky, Missie and Silver who were to be flown home to their birthplace, the Caribbean, after the misery of 19 years of confinement in the South of England.

Such concerted public action made it impossible not to pay tribute to those concerned and to the three dolphins themselves.

L.S.

Bottlenose dolphin

ATLANTIC OCEAN

BERMUDA

THE BAHAMAS

GREAT ABACO IS.

GRAND BAHAMAS

ANDROS IS.

FLORIDA KEYS

U.S.A.

MEXICO

CUBA

GRAND CAYMAN

JAMAICA

HONDURAS

NICARAGUA

COSTA RICA

PANAMA

CARIBBEAN SEA

HAITI

DOMINICAN REPUBLIC

HISPANIOLA

PUERTO RICO

U.S. VIRGIN ISLANDS

VIRGIN ISLANDS

ST. MAARTEN

ST. KITTS

NEVIS

ANTIGUA

MONTSERRAT

GUADELOUPE

DOMINICA

MARTINIQUE

ST. LUCIA

ST. VINCENT

THE GRENADINES

BARBADOS

GRENADA

TOBAGO

TRINIDAD

ISLA DE MARGARITA

ISLA LA TORTUGA

BONAIRE

CURACAO

ARUBA

VENEZUELA

COLOMBIA

Map of the Caribbean

Introduction

The Caribbean fauna is immensely diverse, with fascinating and innumerable subspecies amongst the reptilian, insect, bird, mammalian and land shell families. These life forms first settled on the Antillean land masses when volcanic and glacial activity subsided some 25 million years ago. If we study the fossil beds and geological strata of many islands, attractive enough during these ancient eras for an original marine fauna to establish itself, we are able to understand the birth of what was to become a miraculous, intriguing, imported and sedentary animal community. Assisted by the birds, winds, tides and currents, a complexity of embryonic life

One of the first landfalls for travellers from South America, the island of Grenada.

fluttered and navigated between north, south, east and west. It was a tenacious fauna, adapting itself to specific climatic conditions and territorial dry and rainy seasons of the West Indian island chain.

Seven thousand years ago prehistoric man, no longer able to contain his curiosity, set forth from the American mainland in rustic coracles to investigate the coasts, forests and summits of islands possessed only by the animals. They were not to be disappointed; never-ending stretches of silver beaches, lagoons and cliffs festooned with large populations of edible seashells such as pink conchs, whelks and oysters. Mullet and crayfish thrived in the rivers and streams. Manatees, sea turtles, parrot and angel fish were part of a rich teeming shallow water marine fauna. The manicou climbed the

An Indian dugout (above)

Manatee such as these abounded throughout the Caribbean (above right).

trees, whilst the racoon and agouti raced through the forests. What became of these ancient and lifesaving faunas? Total absence of forethought and a policy of expedience to which the New World discoverers were committed, led to its rapid extinction, accelerated by concentrated hunting and overharvesting. It became an irreversible situation.

When the great land and sea mammals of the north had become too rare to be of interest, man's attention then turned to the southern reaches and other minor life forms. The smaller, lesser members of the realm from marsupial to cetacean now faced pitiless destruction. Where man trod the animals fled, or became part of an historic document. Massive colonies of pelicans, boobies, and frigate birds were subjected to wholescale slaughter. These decimated bird communities disintegrated in the islands, the survivors flying in the direction of their native American homeland.

The fauna of the Caribbean is now fragile, its survival in the balance. This document is a reminder that dolphins now stay far from our shores; they have perhaps at last registered the fate of their kin, suspended lifeless on large dark hooks in fish markets. The humpback whale, on its 5 000 km long miraculous journey south, singing its way to its chosen breeding grounds in the Grenadines, would be harpooned indiscriminately on arrival, both mother and calf.

Whereas the Indian hunted with care and intelligence, the European had no such plan, the hunt was for profit and politics. They introduced many new species of animal life: rodents, oxen, wild boars, mules and horses. Such enterprise resulted in a surprising mixture of animals from different lands and origins. The remaining original fauna now shuns us, and with reason, for surely it can no longer walk through its forest or bush, or swim in its ocean without a feeling of apprehension. It is our task to help these animals survive.

Multiple corals, part of the protective barrier reef bordering many lagoons (opposite).

The last of the tropical seals, the Hawaiian Monk Seal (opposite, top left).

Barracudas live in shallow waters, are curious and extremely intelligent (opposite, top right).

The forest, home to a multitude of birds and animals (opposite page).

A Carib Indian shell midden has formed a beach of Queen Conchs at Ile de Cailles (above).

Neither Arawak nor Yanomami Indian remain today. They treated their new land with respect, but their fate was linked to that of the animals (left).

An ancient Indian settlement, and nesting site for the Hawksbill turtle (above).

Hawksbill turtle

Extinct and Endangered Species

When I first envisaged a handbook on the fauna of the Antilles, little did I realise into what dark ante-chambers the research would take me.

From species to species that for 20 years I thought I had known fairly well, I was to be confronted with documentary evidence that was agonising; the personal observations of many, an accumulation of facts in the space of 12 months from North and South America, the capitals of Europe and Asiatic countries. I had hoped to portray the animals, both marine and terrestrial, as carefree social groups but this I realised was most certainly not the case. Was it then impossible not to describe this very special fauna from chapter to chapter, as doomed and often tortured and miserable? Few readers would wish to be confronted with such a narrative, but I decided the second part of this guide would plead their cause, no matter. I had never imagined that this would be nearly the totality of the text.

During the last four decades alone the following terrestrial species became extinct in the Antillean region:

6 species of insects, *Nesophontides*
7 species of bats
24 species of rodents
and the only wolf species, *Canis niger*.

CARIBBEAN MONK SEAL – *Monachus tropicalis*

Monk seals were widely present in the Atlantic and Caribbean when Christopher Columbus arrived in the Americas in 1492. They were alas, to be rapidly transformed into train oil and hide by an apprentice fishing population transported from the Old World who brought with them their customary bad habit of extensive over-hunting and harrassment. The confiding seal was on the brink of extinction by the late 1800s.

The monk seal was a rare inhabitant of tropical seas, as no other seal had been tempted to investigate the warm waters of the lower latitudes. It appears that this was a behavioural change in the sea mammal rather than an anatomical or physiological modification.

Antonio Mignucci of the Department of Marine Sciences, University of Puerto Rico and Coordinator of the Caribbean Stranding Network, was one of the few people to delve into the life and ways of this extinct species. The Monk Seal earned its name from its resting position. It would hold its head in such a way that numerous folds formed around the nape of the neck, forming a hood reminiscent of a religious cowl. The larger female might have weighed 100 kg and measured nearly 3 m. The fur was brownish-grey and the belly yellowish white. It is thought that mating took place every two years, the pups were probably born during the winter months. They had thick black woolly pelts and measured just under one metre. The last of these seals was sighted on the Serranilla Bank, west of Jamaica, in 1952.

Endangered or threatened species

MARINE MAMMALS
Tursiops truncatus, Bottlenose Dolphin
Globicephal macrorhynchus, Pilot Whale
Megaptera novaeangeliae, Humpback Whale
Balaenoptera musculus, Blue Whale
Eubalaena glacialis, Northern Right Whale
Balaenoptera borealis, Sei Whale
Balaenoptera physalus, Fin Whale
Physeter macrocephalus, Sperm Whale
Trichectus manatus, Antillean Manatee

FISHES
Aetobatis narinari, Spotted Eagle Ray
Epinephelus guttatus, Jewfish
Lutjanus apodus, Schoolmaster
Holacanthus ciliaris, Queen Angelfish
Sparisoma viride, Stoplight Parrotfish
Scarus taeniopterus, Princess Parrotfish
Scarus guacamala, Rainbow Parrotfish
Balistes vetula, Queen Triggerfish
Priacanthus arenatus, Bigeye
Makaira nigricans, Blue Marlin
Tetrapturus albidus, White Marlin
Rhizoprionodon porosus, Sharpnose Shark

CRUSTACEANS
Panulirus argus, Royal Crayfish
Panulirus guttatus, Brasilian Crayfish

REPTILES
Iguana delicatissima, Land Iguana
Geochelone carbonaria, Red-Legged Tortoise

MARINE MOLLUSCS
Strombus gigas, Queen Conch or Pink Conch
Strombus costatus, Milk Conch
Strombus gallus, Roostertail Conch
Charonia variegata, Trumpet Triton
Cymatium femorale, Angular Triton
Cassis tuberosa, King Helmet
Cassis madagascariensis, Queen Helmet
Cyphoma gibbosum, Flamingo Tongue
Conus cedonulli, Matchless Cone
Conus daucus, Carrot Cone

ECHINODERMS
Oreaster reticulatus, Reticulated Starfish
Tripneustes ventricosus, White Sea Urchin

CORAL
Antipathes herta, Black Coral

MARINE TURTLES
Caretta caretta, Loggerhead Turtle
Eretmochelys imbricata, Hawksbill Turtle
Chelonia mydas, Green Turtle
Dermochelys coriacea, Leatherback Turtle

MARINE BIRDS
Pelicanus occidentalis, Brown Pelican
Fregata magnificens, Magnificent Frigate Bird
Puffinus iherminieri, Audubon's Shearwater

TERRESTRIAL BIRDS
Chrondrophierax uncinatus, Hook-Billed Kite or Merlion
Falco peregrinus, Peregrine Falcon
Pandion haliaetus, Osprey
Ortalis ruficauda, Rufous-Tailed Guan or Cocrico
Columba squamosa, Red Necked Pigeon
Leptotila wellsi, Grenada Dove
Amazonia guildingi, St Vincent Parrot
Tyto abla, Barn Owl
Glaucidium brasilianum, Ferruginous Pygmy Owl
Ara macao, Scarlet Macaw
Rhamphastos tucanus, *toco* and *vitellinus*, Toucans

TERRESTRIAL MAMMALS
Didelphis marsupialis, Manicou – Marsupial
Dasypus novemcinctus, Nine Banded Armadillo
Procyon minor, Racoon (thought to be extinct)
Dasyprocta aguti, Agouti

Marine Fauna

The Large Cetaceans

All sea mammals must breathe atmospheric air at regular intervals to survive, a characteristic which makes them different from the oceans fish population. The largest mammal in the world is found in the sea. This is the swift and graceful blue whale who can measure up to 34 m. Although the blue whale is not a native of the Caribbean, many other large cetaceans are. Second in size to the blue whale are the fin and sei whales, who together with the humpback, minke, sperm and bryde whales, measuring from 7 to 22 m, may live to be 80 years old. In all but the territorial waters of St Vincent and the Grenadines, St Lucia and Grenada, these great creatures are protected. In some countries a sanctuary has been established in their breeding grounds.

In 1982 the International Whaling Commission passed a ban on the killing of all rorquals,

Humpback whale

including the humpback, which was not universally adhered to, although an United Nations Moratorium endorsed the ban. By 1984 the decline of the Grenada Bank breeding stock was so extensive that its extinction from the region seemed imminent. Even so, St Vincent was to claim, and be accorded, aboriginal subsistence whaling rights for three years (1989 to 1992) by the Whaling Commission. This quota for three whales in each year was subsidised by other prowhaling nations. $50 000 was a small price to pay for the harpooning of one of the worlds most endangered species. In Spring 1991 two family humpback groups returned to breed on the Grenada Bank. The adults boisterously jostled the young calves in the shallow lagoons, and I watched them with wonder. It was with dismay, regret and anger, that I was to follow the tracking of these same animals and the hunt they were subjected to, for the nature of it was not rigorously aboriginal. Famine was not a reality of the Grenadine Archipelago, and never will be, subsistence whaling in this case seems to be a cultural activity.

A Whaling Museum is to be constructed on Bequia, which will certainly portray the courage of the harpooner, Athneal Ollivierre. Perhaps the moment will also come for the Grenada Bank to become a humpback sanctuary, and we shall once again see these rare whales return to their ancient breeding grounds.

Contrary to all hopes, the 1991 International Whaling Commission meeting in Iceland caused grave concern by dealing several death blows to species struggling for survival. Whaling fleets from Iceland, Norway, USSR, and Japan were supported by St Lucia and St Vincent. The request by Japan for an emergency allocation of 50 minke whales was designed to confuse the Commission; together with a threat by these nations to walk out of the meeting and abide by their own laws. This would have resulted in the wholesale killing of whales and dolphins, making annual counts and population balance uncontrollable with the added factor of pirate whaling in the Indian Ocean, Pacific and Atlantic. Because of this attitude an emergency resolution designed to save the three most threatened cetacean species was withdrawn unexpectedly, sentencing to death these rare sea mammals including the vaquita porpoise from Mexico. Many whaling vessels are notoriously swathed in clouds of mystery when ownership and registry is questioned.

THE HUMPBACK WHALE – *Megaptera novaeangliae* –
The Great Winged New Englander

The story of whales is a hard one in the telling, and that of the annual migration of the humpback breeding stock to the lower reaches of the Antilles and the Grenadine Archipelago is also one of massacre and destruction. The decision made annually by these giant, barnacle covered rorquals to travel south once mating has taken place, is for the survival of a new-born calf. The totally dependent calf could only survive its first weeks in warm tropical waters. Here, during a two month period it accumulates the essential protective insulating blubber needed to survive the long journey northward to boreal waters.

New born, it suckles dozens of litres of milk a day, doubling its size during the first week. The mother is particularly attentive, surrounded by humpback 'nurses' in case of need. These 'nurses' have been known to be males waiting to mate with the mother.

To reach these breeding grounds, in October and November the humpback heads towards the lower latitudes at a cruising speed of 8 to 9 knots. With the coming of spring in March and April, it starts its long run to the krill shoals some 4 500 km north. The miraculous birth of the small baleen takes place during the winter

The gentle Humpback whale will allow a diver to take a ride.

months. Weighing no less than 2 tonnes, it is often born close to shore in the lagoons and shallow bays where the water is warmest. For a 60 tonne female the danger here is immense, but she has waited six or seven years to give birth to her first offspring and from then on her priority is its survival. Every other year she enters into courtship with a chosen male. The courtship of this species is one of the most astonishing of the animal kingdom. Using their greatly extended front flippers for balance and propulsion, and as arms to caress and stroke their partner, they play gently and humorously together for hours. Of all the giant rorquals in the world's ocean the ungainly humpback is an original, a lover of fun and a composer of sweet and melancholy songs of immense complexity, which I was to hear and never forget. Each male has a tune specific to him. These songs echo for miles through the ocean – messages, signals, and an appeal.

Their massive toothless mouths are fringed with multiple feathery baleen plates. The humpbacks are impressive filter feeders, swallowing tons of the cold water krill (small planktonic shrimps or fish such as the sand lance) daily. Krill is scarce in temperate and tropical waters and the humpback stock must diet for the five months it spends there.

60 tonnes of Humpback whale displays its acrobatic agility (above left and right).

A newborn Humpback calf learns navigational skills, balanced on the winged flipper of its mother (below).

The decline of the humpback

The natural life span of the humpback whale is some 80 years. In constant motion, it cruises the ocean seemingly oblivious of so much impending danger and destruction of its kind. It was towards the end of the 19th century, when the massive slaughter of the rorquals had reached its zenith in the North Atlantic and profits were declining for the whalers, that the Nantucket and Norwegian 'killer boats' (as they were so justly called) set their sights on the southward bound breeding stocks. The first expedition to the Grenada Bank was horrendous in its results, with 174 females and calves landed at the whaling stations established off Bequia. No prey could have been easier than the slow swimming calf who unsure of its abilities, remained closely beside its mother's fin and the protection of her great body. So deep was the female humpback's maternal instinct that not even witnessing man's diabolical use of multiple explosives and the harpooning of her offspring could persuade her to abandon her infant now in its death throes. She hauntingly hovered over the mutilated body accompanying it in death to the very slipway of the shore station; a suicidal act of love, for there, she in her turn was slaughtered. The humpback tribe along with its kin was now speeding down a bloodied path to extinction. The 1925/26 whaling fleet that had initiated the killing continued to pursue these defenceless creatures. Then a lull, strangely coinciding with a significant absence of rorquals in the Southern Caribbean, between 1940 and 1960. Through lack of profit the trade became more skilled and directed, with lateen rigged small vessels setting to sea with hand harpoons, and a confrontation more severe than ever before. Between 1982 and 1985, breeding female humpbacks were killed by Bequia whalers, assisted by power boats and yachts.

THE SPERM WHALE – *Physeter macrocephalus*

Sperm whales are the magnificent toothed monsters better known to us than any other for their ability to attain the oceans dark depths. Reducing blood pressure and buoyancy, it speeds gracefully towards the deep, seeking its prey of giant squid. In the Caribbean these cetaceans are not an unfamiliar sight. They have been hunted in recent years off the coasts of St Vincent where the spermaceti oil and flesh are primitively processed. The oil is contained in the huge head which measures one third of the body length. An international moratorium gave these whales full protection, which most nations adhered to. Breeding groups in the Caribbean are far smaller than elsewhere. Stocks have been relentlessly hunted by humans since the beginning of the century, only 50% of their original numbers are thought to remain. 200 000 were killed in the single decade of the 1960s alone.

In every way the sperm whale is unique, for a number of sexually mature females (aged about ten years old) will be under the domination of one superior male, who attains maturity far later than the female at the age of 25. Such superiority may be contested by a younger bull through combat. Calves are born after a 14 to 16 month gestation period and may stay with their mothers for as long as five years. This whale is also killed for its ambergris, a substance extracted from the animal's intestines and used as a stabiliser for perfume.

The seas abounded with the great whales when Columbus discovered the Americas at the end of the 15th century. Men most surely learnt whaling by these great sea mammals coming to them, illustrated by artists engravings from as early as 1577.

The Small Cetaceans

Those we call the small cetaceans in the Caribbean are the little whales. These include the orcas and the short finned pilot whale. The dolphin family is represented by the bottlenose, saddleback, spotted, striped, spinner, bridled, grey, grampus, and the clymene species. With no established laws for small cetaceans their future is not bright. These most ancient, agile and sleek friends of the human race, able to rescue and comfort us on the high seas, have been designated in their hundreds and thousands as target practice, food for mink farms and pet food.

Drift nets, gill nets and purse seines pose the biggest threat of all, world wide, for these beautiful sea mammals. Giant driftnets 145 km long, known as 'walls of death', are employed by Japanese, Taiwanese and Koreans in the Pacific and now in the Atlantic. A driftnet fleet is able to cull over 2 500 km of ocean a night, and it has been calculated that enough of the nets exist to encircle the globe. Such holocausts subject every form of marine life; sea birds, cetaceans large and small to a terrible lingering death.

A United Nations moratorium was passed condemning the use of such nets. In 1992 at the International Whaling Commission meeting, a continued ban on whaling was accepted despite bitter complaints by Japan and Norway. Norway indicated that it would restart whaling despite the moratorium and Iceland resigned from the Commission. The proposal for a whaling sanctuary by 1993 (now potentially in Antarctica) met with opposition and the ¾ majority vote needed to secure a sanctuary could not be guaranteed due to Caribbean prowhaling states. Further decisions await the 1993 meeting in Tokyo.

Even during the final debate, a massacre of 100 Pilot whales around the Faroe Islands was in progress using a new type of gaff (hooked pole) designed to tear the flesh of the animals. It was an appalling and merciless event, with the

A blood bath – Pilot whale carcasses after the kill.

film crew of the Environmental Investigation agency being beaten up. For those who love the long suffering sea mammals the struggle for their survival is far from over.

A purse seine specifically cast for tuna fishing is the most dangerous and deadly form of net for those dolphins that run with the tuna. In any one year as many as 500 000 dolphins are taken this way. On one occasion 200 spinner dolphins were captured in a tuna net off Costa Rica, with only **twelve** yellowfin tuna – the official prey. The United States place observers on the tuna fishing vessels, who monitor the 'back down' procedure imposed by law. This is the partial release of the entangled dolphins. Such an operation however, causes the animals immense stress and is often fatal for the majority of pregnant or lactating females and their young. Sharks are waiting outside the nets to prey on the stunned dolphins. Explosives are also known to be used to hasten the job of rounding up dolphins in secondary nets. It has been proved conclusively that this method permanently damages the animal's hearing and navigational echo location. To avoid restrictions and official monitoring, many vessels register under non-aligned foreign flags.

Traffic in pilot whales, orcas and dolphins is still a thriving commercial business, encouraged by seaquariums. The capture, transport and rehabilitation in confinement as circus performers of adults, and youngsters often still in need of their parents, leads to tremendous stress build up, ulcerated stomachs and early death; all compounded by introverted nervous disorders which the dolphins cannot tell us about. Each capture involves the breaking up of a family group. Orcas are known to be monogamous, and deprived of their partner they are condemned to a life of solitude for as long as they are to roam the ocean. We are now technically able to film all these cetaceans in their natural environment. Such documentaries can be distributed world wide. This is a far kinder way for us to learn about these threatened sea mammals, and perhaps when a small cetacean protection law has been universally ratified, the depletion of these stocks will cease.

ORCA – *Orcinus orca*

A pod of Orcas.

A male and female Orca. Males have an exceptionally high dorsal fin, distinguishing them from the females.

Pilot whales on the high sea.

These beautiful ocean dwellers are the largest and most intelligent of the dolphin family. Their common name, 'Killer Whale' is quite unjustified. On several occasions I have found myself face to face with these cetaceans in an element I respectfully considered at the time to be more theirs than mine.

The first encounter was in 1967, with my water dog, when I was probably as fearless as the orcas, frequently swimming in mid ocean alone. The fins on the horizon were seen first by the Imizer fishermen on shore, whose unhabitual agitation seen from my sea level vantage point was disconcerting. When I turned and scanned the horizon I began to understand why they thought themselves better off than I. My canine companion had already disappeared in a stream of wash, clearing the mile that separated us from land faster than any creature I had yet known. There was little doubt in my mind that had the orca been interested in making me her prey, I had small chance of appeasing her, or swimming faster. The tall fin slowly closed in from behind. With resignation I turned and swam in the direction of land that now seemed a meagre dot on the horizon, from where my faithless quadruped was now safely contemplating the scene with interest. The whale was tracking me. In response to her high pitched clicking sounds a large male arrived and ran parallel. I considered, wide eyed, the tallest of all cetacean fins I had yet beheld.

Ten yards from the steeply shelved beach the whales slowly turned, and with enigmatic expression rolled under me and away. At no time had they become menacing. They had plainly been just intrigued.

Orcas have magnificent black and white markings. Males may measure up to 9 m in length and weigh up to 8 tonnes. Their maximum speed may be 23 knots. They normally travel in groups, or 'pods' of 25 to 30 animals. On the Grenada Bank and in most channels dividing the islands they can be seen migrating from east to west during the Spring.

The capture of live orcas for aquariums is still considered a highly lucrative business. Tremendous stress and suffering is imposed on the animals during capture and transport, bearing in mind their monogamous nature. More than 63 have already been taken from their natural environment to entertain the public in theme parks. In 1990 world conservation groups and humane societies were alerted to a further intended take of four animals for circuses. Sean Whyte of the Whale and Dolphin Conservation Society in the UK, representing a concerned public, was able to persuade Iceland's Prime Minister Hermannsson and his Fishery Department to halt the capture by the Company FAUNA. However, the battle for a final ban on orca exploitation has still to be won.

Tropical Pilot Whales

SHORT FINNED PILOT WHALES – *Globicephala macrorhynchus*

When the blood letting and terrible massacre of the great whale populations had reached its climax, the whalers not surprisingly found themselves with empty oceans and no substantial prey. Their attention turned to another source of income, the smaller cetaceans, previously considered of little interest. Of those destined for slaughter was the short finned pilot whale whose massive pot shaped head contained large quantities of oil. In the ten years separating 1950 from 1960, 48 000 of these creatures were destroyed in Northern Atlantic waters. The wholescale depletion of the pilot whale had been successfully managed by 1971 when only six members of this species were taken. It was now the turn of Caribbean stocks to be hunted throughout the length and breadth of the Antilles to the Guyanas. Makeshift fishing techniques, which caused much suffering to the harmless, shiny, black, 2 tonne whales, were devised by native fishermen groups in the southern Caribbean. In 1991 Japanese and Taiwanese technical assistance helped to develop techniques for the capture of these cetaceans, and improve catch figures.

Pilot whales have strong family ties, travelling together in groups numbering many hundreds and use their efficient echo location system to seek out their primary food source, the vastly abundant schools of squid. The whales pursue this small prey into the abyssal depths to 4 000 m. But the scheme of things belies dramatically the pilot whales survival; this time nature herself is against them. During the warm summer months the squid schools rise to the surface of the ocean and head towards the shallows of lagoons and shorelines in order to reproduce. The pilot whales follow. The danger of mass stranding is imminent at such times, cruelly augmented when men intervene to ensure the whales run aground by speeding the herd to its death from small craft in the rear. Natural mass stranding is most often caused by the instinctive need to assist another of their kind in distress. To return these stranded animals to their natural element is no easy task, needing the concerted will and effort of many. Often only one or two animals can be helped in this way before dying of dehydration.

The Caribbean Stranding Network, at the Department of Marine Sciences, University of Puerto Rico, Mayaguez, has done much to increase public awareness regarding the seriousness of this problem. The hundreds of beached and stranded marine mammals that have been recorded over the past few years represent only a small percentage of deaths. This network of devoted and talented scientists, students and members of the public under the guidance of the area coordinator Tony Mignucci, request any person encountering a marine animal or bird in distress to immediately contact them toll free at 1. 800-462-8124, or 124-2955 and 124-3565, so that action may be taken. Failing this, the nearest Natural Resources Office should be contacted.

THE BOTTLENOSE DOLPHIN – *Tursiops truncatus*

The bottlenose dolphin is one of the fastest swimming members of the dolphin family. They are swift, supple, acrobatic, intelligent and inquisitive, and the most frequently captured for zoos and aquaria. These good natured cetaceans seem to have a permanent tender smile with which they face the world. Rocky, Missie and Silver are members of this species, who after nearly 20 years in captivity and as extraordinary entertainers much against the way their natural lives had been forecast, were to return to the Caribbean and the lagoons of the Turks and Caicos Islands, in Providenciales. This followed a significant, determined and combined effort by the groups 'Zoo Check' and 'Into the Blue', who had launched a national campaign in the United Kingdom for the return of captive dolphins to their natural environment.

Silver coloured with pronounced rostrums, *Tursiops* can measure nearly 3 m and weigh 250 kg. Dolphins are piscivorous, catching their prey with their 80 to 100 conical teeth. They do not use their teeth to chew, but swallow their food whole. Bottlenose dolphins can dive to depths of 300 m. This is a world wide species, breeding every two or three years. One offspring is born after a 12 month gestation period, and may stay as long as four years beside its mother. As sociable animals they live in groups which may number several hundred.

Bottlenose dolphins

The young are always placed in the middle of these groups for protection. Unlike the orcas, bottlenose dolphins are inclined to be polygamous. Courting sequences may last a number of weeks. Dolphins are affectionate animals, attacking only in self defence or in order to protect their young. Their only predator in the ocean itself is the shark. Healthy dolphins will defend themselves by hammering into the underside of these animals at immense speed, causing their enemy fatal intestinal ruptures.

Sirenians

THE MANATEE or SEA COW – *Trichechus manatus*

This is the legendary siren, the mermaid seen and sometimes feared by the ancient mariners who surveyed and charted the world's oceans. Moreri in his Dictionary of 1671, speaks of a 'merman' living off Diamond Rock in the south of Martinique. It had remained on the surface for one whole hour, the sighting was reported to the notary of the nearby town; many men and women witnessed and signed their names to the document. It was, however, certainly none other than the docile, gentle manatee, who innocently explored hyacinth beds and mangrove swamps, and basked in our lagoons. Here the females would breed, and were visitors to every island from Florida to Brazil. Such visits proved fateful; they were hunted by Arawaks as easy prey offering no defence, although it was considered taboo by the Caribs. Europeans quickly exterminated the manatee in all of its preferred haunts in the southern Caribbean, it would survive only in small bands in the large swamp areas of the Greater Antillean Islands. The last sighting in Trinidad was in 1910 when

Manatee

Two Manatee playing off the coast of Florida.

Harry Vincent recorded the harpooning of a 300 kg manatee in the Nariva River.

The female manatee gives birth to one calf, rarely twins, when she arrives at the sexually mature age of 11. She has two nipples tucked under each flipper high up on her chest. A calf weighs 30 kg at birth and may suckle for as long as two years. These creatures have lighthearted love affairs and no binding relationship exists other than between mother and child. Nonetheless groups are extremely sociable and boisterous, and play for hours on end, nuzzling, pushing, bumping, nudging and rolling over each other. Many animals who remain alone for long periods issue plaintive calls echoing through the sea in the hope that such sounds will attract company. Rare are the displays of anger on the part of this unique sea mammal.

The future of the Sirenians

Sirenians are now protected in every part of the world. Only five members of this order are known, which includes the Amazonian, West African and West Indian (or Antillean) manatee, the dugong of the Indopacific has a forked tail much like a dolphin and the Arctic Steller sea cow was rapidly brought to extinction in the late 1700s. In Florida the manatee dutifully keeps waterways clear of weeds and debris, but is often severely injured and killed by speedboats. The mortality rate has increased alarmingly in several areas, including Jamaica and Santo Domingo. Deaths by watercraft over the period 1986 to 1990 show a 60% increase over the previous five years. Although molesting or hunting carries a fine of $20 000 and a possible year's imprisonment in United States territory, it is exceedingly difficult to apprehend poachers. Unless very rapid action is taken, the survival chances of this docile creature are exceedingly bleak.

Sea Turtles – *Cryptodira*

Sea turtles are members of the reptile family and thus air breathing animals. Five species are known to frequent the Caribbean Sea and North Atlantic.

Unable to survive in water temperatures below 12°C, when the cold stuns them and prevents the digestion of food, these marine animals have explored the world's oceans for more than 150 million years, confronting each evolutionary upheaval, repeatedly proving their ability as survivors. Their navigational accuracy and ability is phenomenal. The Sea Turtle was the best loved of Amerindian mythological creatures. In legends it transported men, women and children across the oceans, sheltering them under its massive shell. Dwellings were built in the shape of a turtle back in many areas, and the central house was called the *maloca* (morocoy) meaning 'turtle'.

The rarest of the sea turtles is the Kemps Ridley Turtle, *Lepidochelys kempi*. It is also the smallest and on the brink of extinction. Despite concerted actions to provide total protection for this species, its demise is feared to be near at hand. The addition of new adult breeding females to the now sparse population is too infrequent to bolster the population sufficiently. Recent figures show that no more than 900 adult females are known to exist, with an unknown number of subadults and adults. In the Gulf of Mexico, armed guards protect the species' mass breeding sites. Forty years ago 42 000 females were recorded nesting together in a single day. Recent counts on such breeding grounds record only than 200 nesting females. A large percentage of the remaining Kemps Ridley Turtle are constantly menaced by Gulf shrimp trawls, in particular those without TEDs (Turtle Excluding Devices) imposed by law on United States commercial vessels, but all too often absent elsewhere.

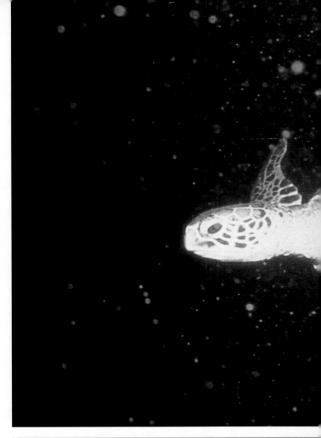

A green turtle surprised during a night dive (top).

Breeding

Many poachers insist that sea turtles lay their eggs in the sea, even when capturing a female coming ashore to breed, in order to justify their actions. The male of the species is never tempted to explore land.

Turtles become sexually mature after a very long subadult period; at the age of 50 in the case of the Green Turtle, *Chelonia mydas*. The growth rate is slow and many animals, if allowed to, may live to be centenarians. Breeding takes place every three to four years, and generation upon generation of female turtles will return to hereditary and traditional breeding grounds. Like the salmon, the turtle seems to be imprinted with the taste of the water of its birth place. Those species of turtles that favour mass breeding, reproducing several times in one season, are thought to do so in order to produce sufficient eggs on one site to counteract the immense predation from different quarters, and thus secure the survival of a small number of juveniles.

Mating takes place at sea, and copulation may last several hours. A single mating will permit the female to lay eggs three or four times in a season. The first nesting is within a month of her encounter with the male. Incubation periods vary from 45 to 67 days according to the species. The eggs are thermosensitive, the sex being controlled by temperature, which for example in the Green Turtle is decisive at 28.7°C, and the Loggerhead 29.5°C. Below this temperature all the eggs will produce males, above they will produce females. Thus turtle populations are strictly governed by climate.

Nesting is a nocturnal ritual for these animals and it is a weary female that returns to the sea at dawn. She excavates a nest in the sand, and according to the species deposits from 30 to over 200 eggs in this burrow, before carefully

The very rare Kemps Ridley turtle, nesting (bottom).

A Leatherback turtle mother returns to the sea after an arduous nights work (top).

Scientific observations and measurements of a nesting Leatherback turtle (above left).

Leatherback turtles nesting (right).

covering it with sand. The eggs resemble ping pong balls, and are soft membraned. The female turtle leaves deep tracks behind her, which despite her diligence are the perfect signal for poachers. The largest of the turtle family, the Leatherback, *Dermochelys coriacea* breeds in the southern Caribbean, Guyana, Surinam and Costa Rica. Hawksbill Turtles, *Eretmochelys imbricata* are solitary in their behaviour and difficult to observe.

Hatchlings

Hatchlings emerge from their eggs by using a special temporary sharp point on the tip of their small snouts, with which they will pick away at the rubbery shell until there is a sufficient opening for escape. It is important for the hatchlings to work simultaneously if they are to evacuate their burrow. The sand falling on the empty shells forms a platform that will allow the young turtles to clamber out on to the beach. Measuring 5 cm long and weighing only 30 g, they turn in repeated circles to determine the exact location of the sea before moving, and are then orientated by the glow of the horizon. Beach front lighting often proves hazardous and may fatally distract the hatchlings. A multitude of predators, both human and animal are waiting and watching both on shore and in the ocean. Very few of these youngsters will survive. Their race to the sea, and for life, is a desperate one. Those that do achieve their goal will swim frantically for two or three days towards the open sea, where they will gain in strength and size to become young adults. During these early years few scientific observations are available. The subadult turtle will return to feeding grounds and shallow waters once it has attained a length of 20 to 30 cm.

A Leatherback turtle hatchling struggles from its shell.

The race for life — Leatherback turtle hatchlings scramble for the sea.

Feeding habits

Green Turtles are herbivores, feeding on turtle grass and other seaweeds. This diet taints its flesh but not the shell. The great Leatherback Turtle feeds on an unusual and dangerous member of the ocean's fauna, the venomous *physalia*, or Portuguese man-of-war jelly fish, being impervious to the stinging cells. Loggerheads, *Caretta caretta* eat molluscs and crustaceans, others eat fish and squid. Sponge and sea squirts are the preferred food of the Hawksbill, who uses his beak to scrape these from coral heads.

The future of the Sea Turtles

All of the ocean's turtle species are endangered due to over exploitation by man. Turtles are vulnerable, gentle creatures, easily captured by poachers during their breeding seasons. Despite serious steps taken by most countries to protect these animals, the recurrent abuse is impossible to control. The Green Turtle, equated with Green Turtle soup, was in the past selected uniquely for its calipee, the edible cartilage that holds the boney underplate in place. Wastage was often 100% and the animal generally left to die a lingering death, its body detached from its shell. The slaughter that follows the suffering and abuse imposed on these animals while waiting to be butchered, overturned to render them immobile, is an ugly business which few can tolerate, and more should witness.

The most endangered reptile in the world is the Hawksbill Turtle. Japan, Taiwan, China and Thailand import more than 50 000 Hawksbill turtlebacks yearly for the 'bekko' trade. The 'bekko' trade is use of the turtle shell for arts and crafts; stuffed turtles are a status symbol in a home, and represent longevity ... for the new owner. Driftnets and trawls are responsible for the rapid decrease in populations, thousands of unaccounted-for turtles disappear this way. The only natural predator of the Leatherback and others of this family is the orca.

International wildlife organisations together with the United Nations are working hard to

Despite her release by the author, the turtle's desperate efforts to escape have caused deep wounds which will make her an easy target for her main predator, the Orca.

An exhausted Leatherback turtle mother ensnared in an illicit net.

The turtle hunt, so often uncontrollable and frequently cruel.

align those countries involved in this massive slaughter, asking them to observe restraint and ensure that TEDs become a permanent part of all forms of fish nets which are instrumental in the accidental drowning of turtles. Although the Convention for International Trade in Endangered Species (CITES) has more than 100 countries signatory to the protection law, those determined to continue trading are adept at finding multiple loopholes when under investigation by administrative bodies.

Seahorses – Syngathidae

Seahorses have slender segmented bodies which are encased in numerous, jointed horny rings. The small, tubular snout is toothless. It is the male that carries the eggs, deposited in his brood pouch by the female. This is an unusual phenomenon rarely observed in other marine species. The father harbours the eggs for four weeks, after which the hatchlings venture from their shelter under the close surveillance of both parents.

Seahorses swim vertically, using their small dorsal and pectoral fins as rotaries which enable them to move in all directions, and using their tails for both balance and an anchor. The species here closely resembles the seaweed of its habitat, where it was feeding on small crustaceans, polychaete worms and other invertebrates. Most seahorses choose to live in an environment into which they can easily blend. These evocative marine animals are relatively rare in the Caribbean.

A seahorse and its algal anchor.

Crustaceans and Molluscs

QUEEN or PINK CONCH – *Strombus gigas*

Strombus gigas is also a member of the endangered species of the world. In all Caribbean countries, over fishing and harvesting during breeding seasons have caused the demise of this economically imporant mollusc. Exploited for more than 3 000 years, it is astonishing that this hardy, exquisite seashell has survived so long. Generally where human population densities are high on land the mollusc is extremely rare in neighbouring waters. Offshore populations in deep water are most certainly those that play the important role of ensuring present day survival of the species.

Females lay several spawn masses per season and these contain as many as half a million eggs. The three week pelagic, or free-swimming, stage of the conch larva is the most hazardous of all as predation by fish, crabs and numerous ocean dwellers accounts for more than a 90% loss.

Discarded Conch shells.
In good hands – The Queen Conch.

These animals initially selected a shallow water marine meadow environment, and prehistoric settlers often established villages close to these highly concentrated shell colonies. Nonreproductive conchs, mostly those which are over 25 years of age, are observed to migrate to depths of 40 m and more.

Great efforts are being made to try to save this fishery and the molluscs themselves in the Caribbean, and to eliminate exportation. It is considered necessary in some countries to halt conch fishing altogether until stocks revive. From Florida to Belize, closed seasons have been recommended and a minimum size take of 20 cm imposed. In Venezuela a licence is required to fish conch. Fortunately the State closely controls this fishery, and stocks have so far remained stable.

The most important breeding grounds for the Queen Conch are in the Turks and Caicos, where 258 900 square kilometres of shallow water exceeds in area the combined remaining Caribbean traditional fishing grounds. It has been suggested that following the decline of the Green Turtle, whose habitat was until very recently the seagrass beds, this now 'underutilised' resource be reseeded with conchs from hatcheries: the final blow for the Green Turtle.

TRUMPET TRITON – *Charonia variegata*

This legendary seashell is also on the endangered species list compiled by the International Union for the Conservation of Nature, (IUCN) and included in the listings of the Convention for Trade in Endangered Species (CITES). A scavenger of extreme merit worldwide, for years the Trumpet Triton controlled the expansion of the lethal Crown of Thorns *Ancanthaster planci*. The Crown of Thorns Starfish extracts the living substance from corals by smothering them and extending its stomach and has seriously damaged the Great Barrier Reef of Australia in numerous locations. The Triton in this case was accorded total protection as an important predator of the destructive and lethal agent responsible for breaking down one of the most needed elements of the ocean's food chain. Caribbean triton generally control underwater pests such as the venemous Long Spined Sea Urchin, *Diadema antillarum*.

Favouring mainly shallow offshore environments, this mollusc has been widely overcollected for the beauty of its shell. The flesh of the animal is rank and strong tasting. Stocks have been depleted in the last 30 years in the Antilles, and the species is now considered rare.

The Trumpet Triton which preys on the illdoers responsible for the massive destruction of coral reefs – the Crown of Thorns starfish and the Long Spined Sea Urchin.

FLAMINGO TONGUE SHELL – *Cyphoma gibbosum*

These brilliant glossy shells live and feed on soft coral in moderately shallow waters. The populations of the three members of this family have been virtually decimated over the past 20 years, bringing them to near extinction. They were the popular pendant of divers. The animal is without any defence and highly visible due to the elaborate mantle patterns which cover the beautiful exoskeleton. Monitoring over the past five years indicates that there is little hope for this species to recover.

Flamingo tongue Shell

SPINY AND ROYAL LOBSTERS – *Panularis guttatus and argus*

Lobsters in general survived fairly well until the turn of the 19th century, when they were suddenly seen as other than fish bait and fertiliser. So profuse was the lobster on the ocean bed and amongst the coral reefs that indigenous human populations had paid little heed to them, and for many years these crustaceans went unharmed. Lobster was considered a food for poor people until canning factories realised what a lucrative business the processing and exportation of this readily available stock could be. By the turn of the century 70% of the population comprising this rich food source had been indiscriminately harvested from the sea. In the Caribbean lobster flesh was viewed as second best to fish and hunted on only a small scale. Until 25 years ago both lobster species in the island chain went unmolested, and bred freely. With the expansion of tourism a fatal blow was

Spiny lobster, from the Bahamas.

dealt to the crustacean and numbers were depleted.

Spiny lobster

Lobsters have a gestation period of nine months. The adolescent period is extremely long and females only start to breed when they are seven or eight years old having attained an average weight of 0.7 kg. This unfortunately relates to the preferred size of catch for fishermen, therefore population numbers are decreasing rapidly. Although a closed season is enforced on some islands from May to October, too many breeding females have been captured in the past decades for the species to reemerge unless a decision is taken to halt the hunt completely for a number of years. As invertebrates lobsters are capable of experiencing considerable pain; their immersion in boiling water is probably the most painful death to be suffered by any member of the animal kingdom.

Indigenous Land Fauna

Species considered indigenous are those that arrived naturally by their own efforts, or on floating islands at the time of climatic changes in the geological quartenary age during the rise of sea levels.

Piping Frog: small frog, large noise.

Reptiles, Amphibians and Terrestrial Crustaceans

CLIMBING FROGS – PIPING FROGS – REINETTES – *Eleutherodactylus*

There are numerous sub-divisions within the family of climbing, whistling, coqui or piping frogs, throughout the islands. Most of the frogs are semi-aquatic, and all chirp and sing: from a minor degree in low dry zones, to the great crescendo that fills the night air of most humid tropical islands of the region. Some people never accustom themselves to this night-long amphibian chorus, others cannot sleep without it. What is sure, is that a few hours before a hurricane sweeps through the land, the call of the tiny frog ceases, as does that of the cricket and every other creature who animates the warm night with its vociferations. The silence at such times is so complete that it is both disturbing and unnatural; a warning that no inhabitant of these regions does not take seriously.

Most of these small frogs are considered indigenous members of our fauna. Active at night, they sleep in damp corners and in air plants during the day. In most cases a dozen or so eggs are laid out of water, developing directly into small frogs after an incubation period of approximately 11 to 20 days. The froglet pierces the egg membrane with its spike tipped snout.

Amphibians are a fascinating species scattered throughout the West Indies and more information about this family is available in the numerous studies carried out by Schwartz and Thomas during the 1960s and published by the Carnegie Museum in Pennsylvania.

IGUANIDAE – *Iguana iguana and Iguana delicatissima* – Common Iguana

Two species of iguana have been identified in the Caribbean, closely resembling each other, which may indicate that these are one and the same species. The variation noted is the pattern of scaly plates surrounding the eyes.

The iguana is a spectacular and impressive reptile, reaching lengths of up to 1.5 m. It is one of the few indigenous members of the land fauna of the Caribbean, although the gregarious colonies which were part of the landscapes of the islands of St Barthelemy, the Saints and the Tobago Keys have been totally decimated. This is a sad statement of fact, as until 1970 these colonies were virtually intact. With the advent of tourism, they were widely hunted and transported to the kitchens of grand hotels and restaurants of exotic foods, mouths taped, limbs bound, fresh and ready for the chef's will. In much the same way they are transported to Asia where they are prized aphrodisiacs: a tortuous

The Caribbean's largest repile, the Iguana.

Green Iguana

and humiliating journey for the most fantastic reptile of the whole Caribbean region. For years I bought and returned them to the wild, until there were no more left to buy.

Hardy, timid and resistant, the iguana spends its days immobile, curved into the slender branches of a glycirellidae or mapou tree. At dawn they leave to rehydrate themselves at water holes or the sea. They thrive on orchid and hibiscus flowers. Of prehistoric origins, the iguana is able to survive in very hostile climatic conditions, constantly regenerating body heat by remaining immobile, storing the sun's rays and calories.

The breeding season of this species coincides with drought. The animal excavates shallow burrows in sand and lays between 15 and 20 soft, membrane covered, oblong eggs measuring 5 cm. In much the same way as the sea turtle, the iguana must choose humid areas for nesting sites as the fragile composition of the eggs favours rapid dehydration. The eggs are much

sought after as food in Venezuela. Here in country villages common belief has it that it is possible to extract the eggs from the females stomach, sew the flesh together again and release the female to continue life as usual. Proof has it that the iguana quickly dies from infection. Eggs normally hatch after three months, and the young iguana breaks free to start life independently and unassisted. In these adolescent stages, they may be the most brilliant saffron and emerald colours. Unsure of themselves, the youngsters will remain hidden in leafy refuges for weeks on end; adults have been seen trying to encourage juveniles to move when otherwise faced with death by dehydration or exposure. Iguanas use their long whiplike tails to warn off potential aggressors and to inflict deep wounds when acting in self defence. Hunted primarily during its breeding season on the last of its island territories, the iguana is on a sure road to extinction in the West Indies. It is unlikely that it will survive into the next century unless protective laws are made in its favour in the southern Caribbean.

GREEN LIZARDS – *Anolis*

There are more than 80 variations of this smaller member of the *iguanidae* family. The species adapts itself to its environment by chromatic variation. They live in wooded areas, on verandahs and in the living quarters of most Caribbean dwellings.

Lizards are diurnal and are particularly sedentary, occupying and defending their territory against any intruder. Most of these creatures will sleep in exactly the same place, on the edge of a frame or the leaf of a house plant, for their entire life span. Those that choose to benefit from domestic protection are quickly tamed with scraps of meat. They are carnivores whose tongues are covered with sticky sensory pappilae

A rare giant subspecies of the Green Anoli, 40 cm long. Grenadines of Granada (right).

'Arthur' the tame household Green Lizard, pauses to pose during a change of skin.

Green Anoli (left)

Male Green Anoli (right)

---

which assist in feeding. The anoli is extremely rapid when hunting its prey.

The main colouration of the lizard is green, turquoise, buff, grey and brown, with diverse darker stripes, mottling and spots. The male lizard has a dewlap (throat fan) which is usually yellow or orange, and is displayed either prior to an attack on another male, when he raises himself high on the tips of his toe pads and sways menacingly, or when courting. Females are smaller and less colourful. Copulation can last for many hours. The female buries each egg individually, excavating a shallow burrow with her head. After an incubation period of several weeks the hatchlings break from the eggs as self-sufficient miniature replicas some 2 cm long.

The green lizard, as with all members of the *iguanidae* family, is preyed upon by birds and felines, and many green lizards may be seen to have regenerated tails. The phenomenon of autotomy (tail shedding) plays a crucial role in their survival. The part of the tail attacked immediately detaches itself from the lizard's body, living a life of its own for some moments, distracting the predator and allowing the thoroughly scared anoli to find a hiding place. The lizards themselves prey on the eggs of others of their kind, but nonetheless are prolific breeders where mongoose have not been introduced. The mongoose is accountable for the extermination of the beautiful *Ameiva* or Ground Lizard which lived on most Caribbean islands before colonisation.

GROUND LIZARD – *Ameiva ameiva*

This is a large sun-loving lizard which can measure up to 46 cm, with a tail measuring twice the body length. The males are most remarkable with a brilliant blue belly. This attractive species has powerful claws on both fore and hind legs. It scavenges during the day, usually in the vicinity of its deep burrow. This lizard is more or less extinct in most islands other than St Barthelemy, Puerto Rico and the Grenadines. It thrives in dry woodland conditions and is common in Venezuela. Those that live close to populated areas will nearly always be around at mealtimes and are able to cohabit with most domestic pets other than cats. Despite its appearance and extremely long bifid tongue, the species is totally harmless and without defence.

Female Ameiva (right)
Male Ameiva (below)

SKINK or SLIPPERY BACK – *Mabuya mabouya*

A very beautiful species of lizard often found living with colubrid snakes. It has a shiny coppery burnished body with short limbs, the back has four dark brown stripes. In the Grenadines most homes will have a pair of these handsome creatures in or near kitchens. The two illustrated lived in the same quarters under observation for five years and were joined by others representing a subspecies whose legs were barely visible. This is an interesting sign of the evolutionary process. A hundred million years ago limb reduction took place amongst the more ancient group of lizards, who thereafter appeared as snakes. This carnivorous species is considered rare in most islands of the Caribbean.

Skinks mating

WOODSLAVE, HOUSESLAVE – *Thecadactylus rapicaudus*
and

COMMON GECKO or MABOUYA – *Hemidactylus mabouia*

Caribbean members of this family are commonly known as gecko or mabouya. The woodslave is a tropical American indigenous species (second in size to the world's largest gecko, the tokay, from Asia) measuring up to 25 cm in length. These are nocturnal creatures, living behind picture frames and under rocks during the day, to become predators of a wide variety of flying and crawling insects at night. Their hunting activities are regulated by artificial light. The houseslave is a pinky-beige colour with a flat, squat body and head; it appears transparent. They have adhesive, suction padded toes with multiple microscopic hooked hairs which allow them to climb vertical surfaces and glass.

Houseslave, or Common Gecko

The woodslave lives in a cool forest environment, blending well with its background, its colouration dark mottled chocolate. These *geconidae* have given rise to much superstition over the centuries. They cannot be thought of as attractive and their common name 'mabouya', designates evil in Amerindian language. They chatter loudly at night, and have caused alarm to many a novice. These lizards have a larynx with two vocal cords which they put to good use emitting alternating notes, which it is thought are used for communication with others of the species. Females lay two or three round, white eggs which have calcareous, heat resistant shells which are hidden under stones, in cracks and under leaves. As with all reptiles, geckos constantly change their skins, which are unusually fine and fragile. The smaller Common Gecko is a trial for housekeepers as once they have taken up residence they reproduce frequently and droppings are scattered everywhere. This factor almost overrules their usefulness in keeping down crawling insects. In several of the many kitchens I have known I could only control the situation by lining the ceilings with cotton.

H. Mabouia is an introduced species, arriving as a passenger on the first slave ships from Africa. It greatly resembles *T. rapicaudus* but never reaches a length of more than 10 cm. According to habitat it will rapidly change colour from pale beige to dark brown. Females lay up

The well camouflaged Woodslave.

to ten eggs at a time. Although they too have vocal cords, they rarely put them to use.

There is a far prettier member of this family living throughout the islands. It is considered indigenous, and a record holder of some merit. It is *Sphaerodactylus parthenopion*, the smallest lizard in the world, rarely exceeding 2 cm in length. It is usually dark brown with a lighter coloured bar placed centrally between the eyes, and another extending from behind. They are sedentary, moving only briefly from their habitat. They feed on minute sugar ants.

SOLDIER CRAB – *Coenobita clypeatus*

Coenobita clypeatus is a member of the crustacean family, a land crab who has very confusing habits. Unfinished by nature, the crab is shell-less with a vulnerable soft stomach and intestinal region. Because of this the young will seek the shelter of discarded mollusc shells. Subadults of the species often live in groups under dead leaves near beaches, adults migrate to rocky hill regions above the beaches, feeding on fruits and scavenging near homesteads. The crab has a massive left cheliped (claw) which is a brilliant mauve, and a weapon of consequence with which it will cling relentlessly to the object of its aggression. They have highly developed sensory and visual organs, and will retreat into their shell and roll freely down cliffs to escape capture.

These creatures repeatedly change shells as they grow, and large adults invariably choose the West Indian Top Shell *Cittarium pica* as an ultimate housing. They select and examine a number of shells carefully before rapidly dislodging themselves from one to the next. Soldier Crabs are an easy prey for fishermen, who use them as bait. The crab travels at some

Soldier Crab

A male Soldier Crab performs a show of dominance as the others retreat into their shells in submission.

speed and his nocturnal outings often take him into the yards of unsuspecting shell collectors, whose shells he shamelessly steals.

LAND CRABS – *Gecarcinidae*

GHOST CRABS – *Ocypodidae*

There are numerous fascinating species of crabs both terrestrial and marine in tropical regions. They are masters of disguise, and veteran burrowers. One of these was to become invaluable as a means of subsistence for migrating populations from the South American mainland 3 000 years ago. 'The Crab Cultures', as they were known, with little knowledge of salt water fishing techniques, quickly observed the expanses of sandy lowlands riddled with the deep burrows of the brilliant blue, red and yellow crustaceans that had colonised these shady zones. The Common Land Crab *Gecarcinus lateralis* was agile and fast moving on land, it often lived in the manchineel forests. The manchineel apple and the sap of this tree are highly toxic, and crabs living in such an environment may be highly poisonous in their turn. Nonetheless as with cassava roots and other food sources, the amerindian was able to extract all the dangerous substances from the manchineel apple itself and add it to his larder.

Land Crabs will climb cliffs to escape drowning.

The Land Crab is nocturnal and hibernates for long periods during drought, keeping itself moist in the deep underlying layers of mud which it evacuates simultaneously with the rest of the colony to avoid drowning during the first torrential rains of the hurricane season. During the months of July and August this species migrates to the ocean where it releases zoeae, young crabs, measuring less than one centimetre in length. The species can be a serious pest for small kitchen garden crops. Able to live on cliff tops to heights of at least 25 m, they may attain a body width of 15 cm with primary claws double that. These crabs are able to climb vertically at great speed. Populations have been decimated on many islands, and exportation abandoned.

Ghost Crabs are a thriving shoreline species of crab. They are considered the fastest of all land crustaceans, able to reach a speed of more than 7 km an hour over short distances. They are extremely industrious, constantly renovating inundated burrows. They have well defined club shaped eye stalks, with shells that imitate the colour of the sandy beaches they live on.

Land Crabs destined for the table are kept in a pen.

A Ghost Crab removes debris from its burrow.

Morocoy

RED LEGGED TORTOISE – *Geochelone carbonaria*

Only one species of land tortoise exists in the Caribbean, which is the Red Legged Tortoise. This reptile is already extinct in many islands of the northern Caribbean although small colonies still survive in the south. In many cases its survival is due to close protection by island residents such as Corrie Wilcox in Grenada, John Caldwell on Palm Island and Jaques Daudin of Union who have bought them, nursed and nourished them. People like these have pioneered and fought for the survival of our local fauna.

This slow moving, totally defenceless tortoise has been hunted for its meat and beautiful gold and brown shell. The domed housing with black and gold hexagonal scales protects an inquisitive and friendly creature. The males are identified by their long tail, with paler and more concave plastron (the boney plate on the underside of the tortoise). Morocoy are diurnal creatures who burrow into loose leaf and cactii or thickets of prickly bush where they will often hibernate for long periods.

Morocoy lay up to five eggs in shallow depressions, which they lightly cover with earth. The eggs are fortunately not considered a delicacy. The tortoises favourite foods are hibiscus flowers, roots, beans, squash leaves and insects. Occasionally it may devour small invertebrates.

In 1972, following two years of drought, I witnessed a fire on the island of Battowia, one of the last breeding grounds of this animal, remaining a natural sanctuary due to hazardous access. The tortoises tried to escape towards the steep and dangerous cliffs. When the fire had been stopped by rock and dust, the entire area was encircled by skeletal remains of the morocoy. After this fire, looters headed towards the southernmost islands of the Grenada Bank to Large Island, and captured hundreds of the

Red Legged Tortoise

creatures who were bundled into airless bags and subjected to illegal export for sale at garden centres.

The tortoise was brought from Venezuela, its land of origin, by Amerindians more than 2 000 years ago. This reptile is a common member of the Llanos faunal system. The meat of the animal is still eaten by the indigenous peoples of the Llanos and until recently, recommended by local clergy as a substitute food during Holy Week. Despite its ability to breed twice in one year, the decline of the morocoy is now so evident that protection laws have been made in its favour in Venezuela. This is also a recommendation of extreme urgency if the Caribbean stock is to survive.

Mammals

NINE BANDED ARMADILLO – TATOU – CACHICAMO MONTANERO – *Dasypus novemcinctus*

The few remaining groups of armadillos are now close to extinction in the remaining areas of the southern Caribbean they are known to inhabit; Venezuela, Trinidad, Grenada and St Vincent. Nocturnal forest dwellers, they live in very deep burrows in sand or earth. Grenada accorded this small mammal temporary protection from 1963 to 1972. During this time the declining group struggled against illicit hunting for survival and the right to reproduce. The female of the species has an unusual mode of reproduction. At the term of a four month gestation period she gives birth to four young who are identical and of the same sex, derived from a single ovum. Four months later the young armadillos show signs of independence.

These nocturnal animals leave their dens at dusk to hunt for insects, vegetables, small invertebrates and carrion. They have a highly developed sense of smell, and discovery of prey has them digging wildly with their long horny claws, noses submerged. They are able to excavate in this manner for six minutes before coming up for breath. They can swim with great agility, and cross rivers. Indian belief has it that armadillos walk the river bed as easily as they walk the forest floor. The armadillo has a fine protection of armour made of scales and bone and is able to roll itself into a ball. The animal is nonetheless exposed to systematic hunting which drives it to exhaustion as it constantly tries to excavate away from the hunter's shovel. Armadillos are more often than not hunted to provide tourists with a speciality dish in local restaurants. Visitors are urged not to encourage the hunt and thus the demise of the armadillo in this way.

Nine Banded Armadillo, or Tatou

MANICOU – *Didelphis marsupialis insularis*

This ungainly marsupial is a unique member of the *sarigue* or *didelphidae* family of very ancient lineage, identified in the cretaceous fossil beds of Montmartre in Paris. During these times it was pursued by the very largest of the Old World's mammals, yet it successfully established, as did the armadillo, a home in the west where others had failed. Native to many of the southern Caribbean islands, it was hunted to extinction in the northern part of the range at the beginning of this century.

The manicou has a long pointed muzzle and cartilagenous ears with round, black glistening eyes adapted to nocturnal activities, its sight is poor during the day. It has sensory whiskers, and a prehensile tail often used for balance.

The female of the species has a marsupiam, or pouch, for carrying her young. After a nine or ten day gestation period, perhaps the shortest of all mammals, the 'neonates', resembling small naked larvae are expelled from the uterus to embark on a perilous trip to the pouch. Their

Manicou

A tame Manicou enjoys some parma ham at Christmas.

Waiting for the death blow. Trapped, bewildered and exhausted, these two were released by the author.

survival depends on the dexterity and speed with which they can climb through the mother's fur and appropriate themselves one of her seven to fifteen teats. Of 40 eyeless, minute embryos, many will die. Four or five of these will ultimately reach adolescence and gambol for some weeks on their mother's back, hanging to the maternal tail on outings. After four months they take to the woods alone where they will seek a safe hiding place in tree tops, in thick foliage, and occasionally in burrows.

The manicou has a somewhat mindless comportment, intrepidly wandering into kitchens and yards, peeling bananas found in baskets, turning over jars and generally leaving a trail of dubious deeds behind him; when confronted he is in no hurry to leave and may eventually be hand fed, becoming part of the family. He is alas easy prey; blinded by bright lights, caught by the tail and stunned. There is no sorrier sight than to see these rare mammals hanging sense-less from the hunters belt, or waiting for the final blow as we see here. Drums are placed under fruit trees with bait to lure them. The two photographed were in a state of shock when set free, they clung steadfastly with their small suction padded feet to the upturned drum. Once urged out, they sat senseless for an hour and then slowly made their way to the hills, their unsteady gait showing signs of exhaustion and stress.

This species is in danger of extinction and every effort should be made to have it protected and removed from the list of culinary delicacies in restaurants. As with the armadillo, the visitor is strongly urged to discourage the practice of eating endangered species by patronising only those restaurants which do **not** indulge in this unnecessary cuisine.

AGOUTI – *Dasyprocta aguti*

The shy, solitary Agouti.

The agouti comes from a line of very ancient, primitive ruminants. These animals are shy and solitary by nature, feeding on shrubs, leaves, fruits and grains available to them at ground level in the shade of the Amazon forest. The agouti has the strange habit of freezing when confronted with scents or creatures foreign to its territory, remaining so for long periods wide eyed and panic stricken. It is uncertain how the agouti arrived in the Antilles, it may have made its way to Trinidad and Grenada on floating rafts. What is certain is that more than 2 000 years ago Indians migrating up the islands of the Caribbean carried live agouti with them. Agouti remains are found in most kitchen middens. The gestation period of this animal is fairly long, 118 days. One, rarely two off-spring are born, with open eyes and soft pelt. Agouti are known to use burrows excavated by armadillos, in Venezuela a well known song exhorts the cleverness of the agouti in this respect. On the Continent they are seriously endangered as their flesh is highly prized. This was the case in the Antilles, and very few members of this probably indigenous species remain today. Small communities are known to exist on Montserrat, although many were destroyed by Hurricane Hugo in 1989. St Vincent and Grenada have diminished feral populations in need of immediate protection.

THE RACOON – *Procyon minor*

Father Pinchon, the eminent French naturalist who studied the fauna of the French Antilles at length, considered the racoon to be one of the first mammalian settlers in the Caribbean. This attractive, striped, bear-like animal has been exterminated in nearly all the islands of the Antillean arc, and today clings to life in the island of Guadeloupe in the vast areas of mangrove swamps and lagoons where it is a protected species. Despite protection laws it is still the target of determined hunters. It is of major importance as one of the rarest indigenous members of the Caribbean terrestrial fauna. *Procyon lotor* is a larger North American racoon, and a frequent encounter on this continent. Barbados paid bounty for the tails of its endemic racoon *Procyon gloralleni*, and filed its last report on this species in the late 1950s.

The racoon's comportment is often amusing, taken offguard sitting on its hind legs, hands joined and in contemplation. It is fussy about its food, and washes it thoroughly before eating, be it fish, shrimp or crab. Racoons are also known to inhabit mountainous humid regions, they are strictly nocturnal. Females give birth to their young after nine or ten weeks gestation, perhaps four youngsters will survive. They remain dependent on their mother for at least 12 months.

Racoon

Mangrove swamp, a favoured habit of the Racoon (opposite page)

Freedom for some (above).

The misery of a 'pet' Racoon (right).

The diminishing number of racoons gives cause for concern. Those animals submitted to cages and chains should be given their freedom, in the hope that they might bolster population numbers by breeding freely.

Insects

The most amazing and numerically diverse members of the animal kingdom are the insects. It would be beyond the bounds of this book to compete with so many knowledgeable authors or even hope to cover part of this wonderful kingdom.

However, two species merit reflection; one is certainly centenarian and the other could have been invented by Disney or Spielberg.

Wild Bees' nest

METALLIC WOOD BORING BEETLE – *Psiloptera variolosa*

No insect on earth lives as long as the beautiful irridescent Metallic Wood Boring Beetle. A strange and extravagant ritual takes place during the Spring months which correspond to the end of Carême, or drought season. Preferring above all other shelters that of the Guava tree, these beetles will, in much the same way as the hermaphroditic *crepidula* mollusc, pile themselves one on top of the other in order to attain the female of the species and breed.

The larvae are deposited in timbers, beams, and supports. The embryonic stage is one of the longest known in nature's kingdom; 30 years. The adult beetle may live to be more than 100 years old, to which the larval stage may be added. The brilliant irridescent colour of the larger female made her so attractive to man that her wing cases were treasured and sought after for jewellery.

As a centenarian, the Metallic Wood Boring Beetle is the longest living insect in the world, the larval stage alone takes 30 years.

LONG HORNED BEETLE – *Lagochirus araneiformis*

The Long Horned Beetle is rarely as large and as intricately sculptured, or as co-operative, as the specimen that remained in my own home for many years. These beetles have antennae that are three times the length of their bodies and have the bad habit of feeding on wood. They deposit their larvae in extensive channels of superstructures which they survey constantly. They are indigenous to most dry zones of the Caribbean Islands, but are not considered common.

Resident Long Horned Beetle makes himself at home.

Long Horned Beetle (below).

Termites

Termites are extremely organised. These tiny creatures are known to build the highest of all animal mounds throughout the tropical regions they inhabit. Termitaries are built from earth and wood mixed with the creatures saliva, this combination provides solid hard walls and cool conditions for the many thousands of termites that work and live within the colony. Under the domination of a king and queen, the workers keep the termitary well ventilated and in a good state of repair, whilst soldier termites defend. There is a special royal chamber at the base of the mound which houses the royal pair, adjacent tunnels are devoted to the rearing of the young by nurses. Termites are blind, which makes their social structure intriguing.

In the Caribbean most colonies are attached to the trunks of trees which they inhabit and often destroy. These creatures are severe pests to our region as they are highly destructive of properties, both in wood and cement. Many chattel houses succumb to termite activities after a period of 30 years of constant invasion.

Termite nest

Terrestrial Molluscs

BEE HIVE SHELL – *Cerion Uva*

Returning some twenty years ago to England from the West Indies, where molluscs had captivated me by their intricate beauty, I visited the famous London natural history shop 'Eatons'. In a back room showcase I discovered two very strange land snail specimens that had been part of an Antillean collection compiled during the mid nineteenth century. The *Cerion uva* were from Curaçao, and I was unsure where this island was to be found in the Americas.

Seventeen years later and all the wiser, I explored the strange limestone shelves of Curaçao which were covered with a dense growth of *opuntia* cactii. Each cactus plant was heavily burdened with ever-multiplying colonies of bee hive shells. This land snail had established residence in villages, towns, plains and cliffs. It had survived in the unusually dry conditions of the three Dutch islands, Curaçao, Bonaire and Aruba which had most probably never been connected to the South American mainland. Life forms here had evolved and adapted themselves to specific climatic change. This species is unique to the three islands. Its breeding capabilities are remarkable as it is constantly submitted to excessive heat and long periods of drought.

Beehive Shells

Amazon Tree Snail climbs a candle in bush camp.

Birds

BROWN PELICAN – *Pelecanus occidentalis*

The handsome pelican is a symbol of the West Indies, appearing on numerous national flags. Despite this he has been sorely mistreated and hunted to extinction in many Caribbean islands, remaining indigenous essentially only to St Barthelemy and the Grenadine archipelago. Even here numbers have decreased, and the largest and most familiar populations will now be found on the offshore islands of Venezuela and its coast.

These large sea birds usually follow sprat shoals, which is their principal food source. The vertical spin dive executed from a great height

Brown Pelican, symbol of the West Indies (left).

Pelicans and fishermen in Venezuela; friendly rivalry?

A fishing boat is taken over by the 'second shift'.

is of extreme precision, often taking place in shallows over rocky bottoms. These plummeting birds whose weight must be multiplied tenfold on the downward spin, rarely injure themselves by ensuring minimal immersion. Their large, distensible pouch when filled with fish is the target of the ever attendant scavenging Laughing Gull, *Larus atricilla*.

These are outsize birds more than 1 m tall, with a wing span of 2.3 m. They are probably the most silent of all sea birds. Caribbean flocks of pelicans rarely outnumber 20 individuals, whilst mainland flocks may be composed of several hundred. Mass breeding is customary on small offshore islands. Two eggs are laid, and both male and female attend them during the four week incubation period. Fledglings are usually well feathered by 10 or 12 weeks. When any distance is to be covered the flight pattern is most often in single file with a senior lead bird establishing the rhythmic wingbeat. Pelicans were also part of Amerindian mythology and art, 1 500 years ago ceramics were frequently decorated with pelican effigies.

CRESTED HUMMINGBIRD – *Orhtorphyncus*

Hummingbirds are the most fascinating of the Caribbean avifauna. Minute and brilliantly coloured, they are warm blooded with a very high metabolic rate which permits the enormous output of energy their life span (approximately 10 years) demands of them. These creatures are not able to glide, but must maintain a constant and rapid wingbeat if they are to remain in the air.

The crested male is very aggressive and will fight to the death for a territory or during courtship. Females will nest in house plants, where they appear to feel secure, although nesting sites have often been observed to be otherwise. The one illustrated is a cactus plant on a beach, where the strong swell quickly washed away the nest and two white oval eggs. The eggs are soft membraned at one end, reinforced instead by numerous small pleats. This probably helps the young to hatch, which they do following a 16 day incubation period. Fledglings spend a minimum time in the nest, and are given lessons on wing beat methods as they perch facing inwards on the edge of a nest only the size of a silver dollar. They rarely return to the nest once they have taken flight.

These birds are true lovers of honey, sugar and pollen, all necessary to maintain their high diurnal calorie output. There are six West Indian genera of hummingbirds, ranging in size from 6 to 23 cm. At one time they were captured, stuffed in life-like poses and sold to tourists; the trade was successful because of the exquisite irridescence of their plumage. This commerce fortunately died out in the French islands in the early 1980s.

A humming bird nests in an Opuntia cactus, also a favoured home of the Beehive Shell.

A rare St Vincent Parrot. The St Vincent Zoo is attempting to revive the species with a breeding programme.

Distinctive Species of the Venezuelan and Trinidadian Delta Regions

CROCODILES, ALLIGATORS AND CAYMANS

An alligator chews on a discarded fizzy drink bottle.

Few records exist of alligators and crocodiles, the largest of all reptiles, migrating to the Caribbean islands. *Caiman sclerops* is a distinct and rare form endemic to the swamps and delta regions of Trinidad. Despite the ease with which these reptiles might have reached the Grenada Bank during the ice-ages to favour their distribution throughout the Antilles, small evidence exists that they made such progress. In 1910 an

Orinoco Crocodile did, however, cross the 150 km separating its place of origin, Venezuela, to be washed ashore in Grenada. This happened during September, when the Trade Winds turn to the south and currents are perhaps more favourable. It is also a time for seasonal flooding in the Venezuelan deltas. A second crocodile was to make a landfall on the Windward coast of Carriacou in 1928, but according to those who witnessed this arrival the animal died of exhaustion a few days later.

Alligators are generally nonaggressive, but this has not prevented them being widely overhunted for their skins. Alligators breed between November and February. Choosing suitable areas on sandy river banks, females excavate cavities 50 cm deep and lay from 20 to 50 eggs. The eggs are then carefully covered with the same sand and debris, to make the nesting site invisible to likely predators. The eggs hatch after seven to eight weeks, and the mother is known to carry her young in her mouth with extreme care.

The crocodile plays an important role in keeping rivers, swamps and deltas free of unwanted parasites and vermin. Due to its usefulness and the general depletion of major stocks, they are now protected by law in most South American countries. North American species, indigenous to the Florida swamp areas, benefit from similar arrangements.

The Speckled Cayman, illustrated, from South America is one of the most endangered of all species.

The rare Speckled Cayman

LESSER ANTEATER – *Tamandua tetradactyla*

The Lesser Anteater lives in the forest regions of Venezuela. As with the four different species of South America anteaters, the tamandua plays an important role in eliminating vast quantities of ants, termites and parasites that are dangerous to both homesteads and crops in general. All the members of this extraordinary family are in grave danger of extinction due to uncontrolled hunting of the species and destruction of their habitats. The Lesser Anteater spends most of its time in quiet, shady tree tops and branches. It measures 60 cm and has a prehensile tail. The fur is golden yellow.

Females give birth to a single young after a six month gestation period. Adolescents become independent after 12 months. Anteaters have exceptionally long tongues with a sticky substance assuring maximum adhesive performance. The creature delves into anthills and termite mounds, tearing at them with its strongly clawed forelegs. Although slow moving, when forced to defend itself the animal will clutch its opponent in an embrace which is virtually impossible to break and often fatal.

Lesser Anteater

TAPIR or 'THE AMAZONIAN BULL' – *Tapirus terrestris*

This large animal, descended from the race of ancient elephants, is a secretive inhabitant of the South American delta and forest regions. Silent and nocturnal, it feeds on the thick vegetation of wetlands, wading and swimming through water hyacinth beds either alone or perhaps with a mate. Weighing over 250 kg and measuring 2 m in length, its hide is smooth with sparse hairs on the flanks. It has a prominent elongated snout.

These are territorial animals and define their

The 250 kg 'Amazonian Bull', the retiring tapir.

boundaries in the most unusual manner. A gland found close to a poor sighted eye secretes a liquid that is virtually indiscernible, contrary to normal mammalian excretions. In this way the tapir lays his scent with much cunning, as it is impossible for man, his main predator, to detect. Thus our friend the tapir has a fair chance of moving through his territory undetected, searching for his favourite food of palm dates, river plants and small shrubs. His aquatic prowess and ease, however, are remarkable when danger threatens.

One of the tapirs more formidable opponents is the all-powerful jaguar. Only strong adult tapirs are able to fend off such an attacker, after which the tapir speeds crazily into the dense cover of swamp or forest.

Females give birth to one young, born after a 14 month gestation period. The youngster is brown with horizontal stripes which disappear after six months.

Amerindians considered this animal the greatest of prizes and the most valuable of gifts, which they would carry live in their great canoes from the mainland when travelling to the islands. This South American mammal is also intimately associated with an ancient Venezuelan legend: the Indian Queen, Maria Lionza of Yaracuy, highly venerated in the Sorte Mountain regions. Maria possessed many supernatural powers, and her faithful ally and steed was the 'Amazonian Bull'. Today, Maria Lionza's Bull must flee deeper into the forest, as his swamp and forest habitats are destroyed and rogue hunters lead him down the path of extinction.

'It is said his piteous moans make the tiger relent and turn out of the way. These are the only weapons of defence which nature hath given him.'
Charles Waterson, Wandering in South America, 1825

THREE TOED SLOTH, AI, HEEAY or LOGGURREE – *Bradypus tridactylus*

A baby Sloth

A Three Toed Sloth decends to earth on his weekly outing.

The South American sloth family are considered by Amerindian ethnic cultures to be the sacred animal of the forest. They are probably the most sedentary and unmoving of all terrestrial mammals. The Three Toed Sloth figured here has shorter fur than others of the family and is strictly aboreal, living a solitary life more often in humid forests than the lowlands. Sloths are diurnal and spend their lives hanging upside down, suspended by the highly curved claws at the end of their long, thin arms. Sleep is the sloth's primary occupation and for the few hours it stirs itself from such torpor it will quietly ingest its single food source, the cecropia tree leaf. Unlike all other ruminants it has four stomachs.

The sloth has few predators and rarely leaves its treetop bower. Its main activity away from the den is to relieve itself. Once a week the sloth comes to earth, and in exactly the same spot each time will defecate and urinate. Both products are highly odiferous, and it is thought that this action is one of survival and a way of notifying another sloth of a possible courtship, or rare encounter. The gestation period is from four to six months. One cub is born, and will suckle for ten weeks. After 12 months the young sloth leaves its mother to live independently. The male of the species looks as though it has been branded, bearing a deep brown mark down the middle of its back.

All animals of the Amazon forest now live at risk from the increasing network of roads transporting mainly heavy traffic. Imagine a young sloth trying to cross such a highway in its forest territory. I saw a yearling attempting such a feat, to be hit sideways by an uninterested motorist. Before I could reach it, and I ran fast, a second vehicle had delivered it a fatal blow. Traffic through the Amazon forest should be regulated, with strict speed limits. Time is money for those who seek to exploit this unique part of our planet, and the fauna of little importance. The creation of these deadly routes across the animal's territory is an added hazard for their survival. Again a solution has to be found.

CAPIBARA – *Hydrochaeris hydrochaeris*

This is the largest rodent in the world, and a member of the Venezuelan Llanos or delta region fauna. The capibara may weigh up to 60 kg. Their feet are palmate to help them travel from inundated forest to savanah. The government authorises controlled, licensed hunting of this animal during January and February; both meat and pelts are commercialised. This period corresponds to the dry season in the deltas when hundreds of capibara group together around water holes. Fortunately capibara are able to reproduce twice a year, giving birth to up to eight young after a four month gestation period.

The reproduction rate presently manages to keep the population numbers stable. Males are highly protective of the group and when the hunt commences, they will seek to defend young and females by forming a circular barrier and in consequence are the first to die. The hunt is cruel, the animals are either stunned or paralysed by blows to the spinal cord, to be killed 'en masse' later.

Captive baby Capibara

Adult Capibara

Introduced Species

A series of four stamps representing 'Barbadian' Wildlife, but only the Red Legged Tortoise (morocoy) is truly indigenous.

GIANT TOAD – *Buffus marinus*

This indigenous South American species is one of the largest in the world and has been successfully introduced into most islands of the Caribbean. Its main use is thought to have been to control insects such as cane beetles, and venomous snakes. Snakes preying on the toad will die a rapid death caused by the poison glands found above and behind the eyes of the amphibian, now irrevocably in its digestive tract. Revenge for the toad is sweet if posthumous.

Giant toads are commonly attracted to cultivated areas and gardens, specifically those with water sources, although they are not at ease as swimmers and may quickly flag. One of my early experiences of this family was in the south of Martinique in the early seventies. A family

The monstrous Giant Toad, as large as a side plate and armed with poisonous shoulder glands that can kill most things witless enough to swallow it.

group of toads had established itself in an airy closet in the flagstone hall of the great house I lived in. They joined the domestic mammalia of the household without fail at dinner time, sitting behind these in order of importance, waiting for scraps. The dogs, cats and others felt some respect for the toads, and the mixed group tolerated each other well. When I was expecting important guests who would stay for some days, I thought it better that the toads feed elsewhere for a while. I captured all four in a large wicker basket, put them on the back seat of the car, and drove them some 8 km across the bush to an abandoned sugar mill. Creatures of habit, obstinate and in this case determined, they all reappeared at the main door when dessert was being served that evening. They had won their cause.

Giant Toads have an extremely high reproductive rate. Mating takes place in shallow water and the female's eggs are fertilised externally by the male. The egg-laying process can last for nearly half a day.

WILD PIGS AND BOARS – *Sus scrofa*

Wild Pig

In 1492, European man found himself on the shores of tropical islands he knew little about. He had, as insurance, brought with him his own living larder, as had the Indians before him. This larder included wild pigs, who rushed to the forests and disappeared from view. There they bred happily, thrived and multiplied.

Their masters intention was nonetheless to be sure of a good and fresh provision of meat, should one day they return to these shores, which they did. As quickly as the wild pigs had multiplied, they were to be decimated when the first hunter-settlers established gardens, fences and homes. Such tempting fresh shoots with memories of the old world for the pigs, brought them quickly homeward. To track a pig was a tiresome business and inately lazy under the tropical heat, the comfortably seated settler could shoot 30 or 40 a day as they nosed their way towards his shadowed balcony. 'Now,' says Père du Terte 'the situation was such that our men were rowing up wind like galley slaves to seek out the more chaste and wilder pigs, and this exposing the hunters to the miseries of weather, biting of mosquitoes and sand flies endlessly.' Human wisdom once again seemed lacking when the animals were in view. Sows, lactating or pregnant were hastily shot, and the once-precious stock rapidly destroyed.

It was then decreed by law that 'whosoever take shot' at any of the remaining animals would be subjected to severe penalties. Seemingly reassured by such laws the wild pig was now unceremoniously scavenging the educated gentleman's vegetable plot throughout the West Indies. The planter found the situation unjust and intolerable so, unable to shoot the pig, he cleared the land. The pigs returned to the hills and forests to eat just as well, and continued breeding. Even so, once again man lost all sense of reality and completed the extermination of the hardy, adaptable, wild pig. At the beginning of this century not one remained in the hills.

GREEN MONKEY – *Cercopithecus aethips* (Barbados and St Kitts)

MONA MONKEY – *Cercopithecus mona* (Grenada)

The wild primate population of the Caribbean is of African origin imported from The Gambia and Senegal during the 17th century. Both species were hardy creatures, surviving any of the New World monkeys that may have been imported at earlier dates from South America by Amerindians. Primates evolved 60 million years ago and include more than 182 different species. The Mona Monkey is native to Grenada and the Green Monkey inhabits the islands of Barbados and St Kitts.

Intended as an amusing gift for homesteaders the Green Monkey quickly became a pest for farmers as it enjoyed mangoes, papayas, bananas and most of the tropical fruits which it had found naturally in its land of origin. The monkey adapted well to his new tropical home, breeding yearly. Barbados farmers lost up to 40% of their crops to the primate annually, and a bounty of $5 a head was put on the animal. This seemed hard on a monkey who would have preferred to have been left alone in the first place, in his forest on the other side of the ocean. More recently, over a period of ten years, 1 500 wild Green Monkeys have been exported from Barbados for medical research. This is controlled to some extent by the Barbados Primate Research Center who pay $50 for each monkey brought to them unharmed in the special traps they provide to the public.

The Barbadian Green Monkey

These monkeys live in family groups of 15 to 20. Usually only two adult males dominate the group. They are diurnal creatures, living in the tree tops of the northern forest ranges. Females give birth to one young after a gestation period of five and a half months; the infant is hairless and a bluish colour. The adult monkey is golden-brown and grey. It is the flecks of olive green that, in some lights, give an impression of a green monkey.

The Mona Monkey is indigenous only to Grenada and lives in the Grand Etang volcanic crater lake region. They are more aggressive than their counterparts of Barbados and St Kitts, and may weigh up to 27 kg when mature.

They are presently hunted for their meat, and are considered destructive of bird life and cocoa plantations, although their numbers were greatly diminished by Hurricane Janet in 1955. This is an attractive, lively species, with a greyish brown coat and white band of fur encircling the face. The future of this species is very uncertain. This is the recurring fate of so many species initially displaced for human pleasure, then subsequently maligned and decimated.

Mona Monkey

BURMESE MONGOOSE – *Herpestes a. auropunctatus*

The mongoose was imported from Asia during the latter part of the 19th century to control the rat infestation of sugar cane fields. He is also capable of dealing with the lethal *trigonocephal* of Martinique and the Fer de Lance snake in St Lucia. The mongoose was industrious, proving his dexterity and efficiency in many cases. Mongooses quickly established themselves in those islands whose main economy was sugar. They were later maligned as pests, in much the same way as other introduced species were, and an eradication programme was established in many British Colonies.

The mongoose hardly deserved this treatment; he was after all inclined to be friendly and establish himself as a domestic pet. In Guadeloupe one of them was to appoint itself

A Barbadian stamp celebrates the mongoose.

A caged mongoose awaits his turn to fight in the snake-pit. Quick and alert, the mongoose is invariably triumphant.

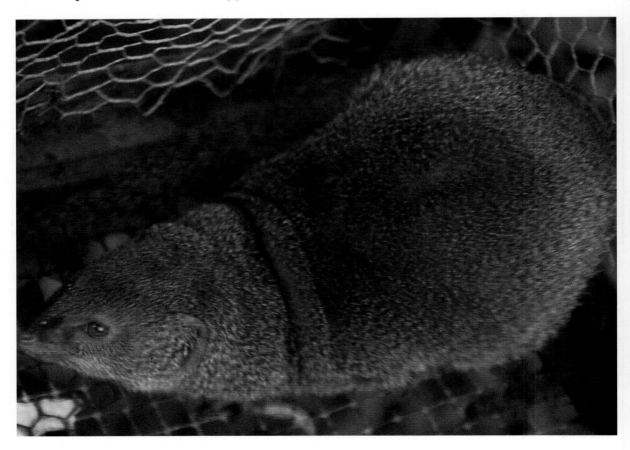

a member of our kitchen staff; it was impossible to move a pot, pan, tool or utensil without it peering out at us like some optical illusion on each occasion. These creatures are full of cunning and their normal diet is one of eggs, reptiles, amphibia and also farmyard fowl. One of the most popular sports in Martinique is the Mongoose-Snake combat. The snake has yet to prove himself a worthy opponent for this rapid and active carnivore.

SCARLET MACAW – *Ara ararauna*

BLUE AND GOLD MACAW – *Ara macao*

'Eric', a Gold and Yellow Macaw, rescued and rehabilitated following illegal trafficking.

These magnificent birds are indigenous to the South American mainland and Amazon forest regions, where the Scarlet Macaw is one of the most endangered tropical bird species in the world. They have been subjected to intense trafficking over the past five years, from their countries of origin through the Caribbean Islands, to Beijing, Bangkok, Hong Kong and other Asian destinations. Many birds die during transport in atrocious conditions. The profits are so high on one bird that the mortality rate is of no consequence to the traders. By the time world environmental organisations took action, at least half of the species involved had declined or disappeared altogether.

This illegitimate trading activity came to a serious climax in 1989 when more than 300 of these beautiful parrots were illegally exported from the Amazon Basin through the Caribbean, for further transportation. The macaws in many cases had broken feet, wings, and necks. Most of them were covered with parasites and pitifully stressed and traumatised, wildly pulling at their chest plumage and any other feathers they could reach.

The highly endangered Scarlet Macaw. 'Oberon' is another escapee, but these lucky birds are only the tip of the iceberg (opposite).

'Oberon', free to fly on Carriacou.

Two of these macaws were to know freedom of a sort when purchased by Wendy Cooper who lived in the wooded region of High North on the island of Carriacou. She nursed the birds back to health, they blossomed rapidly and were eventually able to live freely in the thick forest, adapting themselves to the local grains and fruits. In the Amazon forest of its origin the macaw feeds on the wallaba tree fruit. The pods of this tree are large slender bells and a family of macaws feeding in these trees is easily located by the resonant music created by the falling cases. Wendy Cooper's two macaws, 'Oberon'

and 'Eric', are presently semi-dependant on a regular dietary complement from their owner, but venture further afield with time. Should the birds breed in the future, a small colony on the island may be envisaged.

The macaw is certainly the most sought after bird in the jungle. Indian hunters make fires, producing hallucinogenic smoke beneath the tree the bird lives in. The macaw is quickly intoxicated and falls to the ground to be re-animated by its new master who blows air up its nostrils. The birds are diurnal and can be seen flying in pairs across forest and river to their nesting sites each evening. The flight movement, most often in unison, is one of the most wonderful sights the forest has to offer. Their cry is raucous and their sharp, strong, curved beak a weapon of some consequence. Females lay two eggs which hatch after four weeks. The fledglings will remain in the nest for three or

Exposed to illegal trafficking almost to the brink of extinction, Gold and Yellow Macaw fledglings like these rip out their own feathers in confusion and disorientation.

four months before learning to fly and leaving the nest.

The *Ara macao* is in Category 1 of the IUCN endangered species list. This indicates that the species is in danger of extinction unless all further trading, considered illicit, ceases. Tropical bird species are also known to be submitted to the horrors of transporting drugs internally. The bird in this instance is no more than a packing case, as the value of heroin or cocaine it may be carrying exceeds by far the street value of the bird itself. Any person encouraged to buy macaws should think twice, and in all instances in the case of the Scarlet Macaw, refuse the temptation and report the trading if the species is to survive. Zoological Institutions in the United States are specialised in the recuperation and destressing of endangered tropical bird species, and encourage breeding. If tropical birds subjected to such trade are not able to return to their country of origin upon official confiscation, the Amazon in this case, which seems the most natural and humane outcome for these creatures, the only alternative is that of confinement. Public opinion in such situations should pressurise governments and other authorities to repatriate all tropical bird species to the rain forest where they belong, rather than to condemn them to cages and further imprisonment.

Other Introduced Species

EUROPEAN RABBIT – *Orytolagus cuniculus*

This species was widely raised for its food value and arrived in the Caribbean with the first ships from the New World.

HOUSE MOUSE – *Mus musculus*

Introduced at a very early stage into the Americas by the first immigrants from Europe.

NORWAY RAT – *Rattus norvegicus and* BLACK RAT – *Rattus rattus*

These two rodent species arrived with the voyages of discovery, and have successfully colonised the length and breadth of the Americas. Feral or wild populations of the Norwegian rat exist, the creature is attractive with fluffy white underparts and soft grey fur. Both species are of outstanding intelligence. The latter may well invade homesteads but only at night, living in nests or burrows in the wild.

FALLOW DEER – *Cervus dama*

The fallow deer is found on Antigua, Curaçao, Barbados, and the Hispanic islands. It is believed that these were imported during the 17th and 18th centuries more for decorative purposes in private parks than for their food value. In Curaçao this species now lives wild.

The Future of the Fauna in the Caribbean

'Never doubt that a small group of
thoughtful committed citizens
can change the world, indeed it's
the only thing that ever has.'
Margaret Mead

Caribbean Reef Shark; an undeserved reputation.

Although sharks are not heavily represented in this volume, this in no way implies that many species of Caribbean *carcharhinidae* and members of this family associated with reefs, are neither present nor endangered. Indeed many of them are. They are not the lethal killers they are made out to be, they have systematically been slaughtered because of this misunderstanding. Very few recorded accidents in the Caribbean have been attributed to these creatures. Although they should be observed with caution, the pleasure of watching the immense grace and beauty of these ocean dwellers is lost to most of us through unnecessary and hereditary fear. Sharks, in much the same way as horses will, sense their dominance quickly. More often than not they will continue on their way without demonstrating any interest at all in a casual observer. Young sharks enjoy surfing on reef breakers at evening time, and are as curious as they are timid.

Paying for a crime he did not commit, a harmless White Tip Shark hangs, caught by a longliner vessel.

The Blue Shark has been decimated on the high seas by driftnets. Their case is well demonstrated in a National Geographic documentary which vividly depicts what happens when a driftnet sets to work. A second documentary called 'Where Have all the Dolphins Gone?' produced by the Marine Mammal Fund and the American Society for the Prevention of Cruelty to Animals, tells the tragic story of the **six million** dolphins killed in the last 30 years in purse seines. This heart rending documentary of an ongoing tragedy should be part of all school and college environmental education programmes, both private and public. I would not deny that sitting through such documentaries is a harrowing experience. The Wildlife Protocol of the Cartagena Convention ratified in Martinique in 1990, and with a membership of 300 000, advocates the protection of all

Freedom. But what about the future?

marine mammals in our waters. It is stated that currently these animals are not given the priority that their survival and protection requires. As our Caribbean nations develop, our whale, dolphin and manatee populations will eventually be looked upon as one of our most significant legacies for future generations, **if** protection of all Caribbean marine mammals has been secured. For this to be so, more than words on paper are necessary. Awareness from the very youngest to the oldest of our citizens is now urgent. For this, a certain courage and determination is necessary.

In June 1991, three major marine ecological disturbance alerts were recorded throughout the

region. Sea urchin mass mortality: *Diadema antillarum* (Black Longspined Sea Urchin), reminiscent of the 1983-1984 mass mortality throughout the region; coral reef bleaching, and turtle tumour outbreaks. All of these are being researched and a large scale effort to pool information is needed. Observations should be sent to Bert Williams or John Grizzle,
Department of Marine Sciences,
University of Puerto Rico,
P.O. Box 908,
Lajas,
Puerto Rico 00667.

A notable and laudable success in the rescue of captive rare and endangered species was achieved after seven months of diligent work by the members of the Grenada Society for the Prevention of Cruelty to Animals. On 31st December 1991 a specially chartered aeroplane flew 200 exotic birds and animals from their plight in the 'zoo' in the Botanical Gardens to the safety of reputable breeding institutions in the United States. All the travellers arrived alive and in good condition, an accomplishment in itself but previously impossible had the animals been transported in their original condition.

In the words of CITES (the Convention on the International Trade in Endangered Species): 'Without the tireless efforts from GSPCA volunteers, there is no doubt in (our) mind that these animals already under stress and suffering from neglect by their previous owner would have died.' As the President of GSPCA, John Albanie, comments, 'The operation served as a signal to those elements that deal in the barbaric trade of animals caught in the wild, that their medium-term prospects are non existant. There is enough international outrage at their activities for such a trade to be outlawed ... little Grenada's SPCA have shown how these operator's wings can be clipped – at around neck level.'

Most terrestrial faunal species of the Caribbean region featured in this work are urgently in need of special attention and protection laws. The reality of the problem is that we are generally unable to coordinate our feelings and needs and equate them with human and economic factors. We all too often refuse to accept the clear evidence provided by scientific monitoring and observation of our fauna over the past four decades. We seem unwilling to avert disaster. Nevertheless, I believe that greater awareness must inevitably lead to the beginning of a solution.

The ultimate humiliation, turtle-head bookends.

Index